Knitting Journal

Crafter's Choice
New York

Cover design by Monica Elias

Interior illustrations and design by Alicia Freile
Written by Nancy W. Hall
Edited by Victoria Hyun

Printed in the United States of America

Did you ever see a fabulous sweater in a shop window and say to yourself, "I could knit that!?" Here's the place to sketch it so you don't forget its wonderful details.

Did you ever finish a pair of toasty socks for a friend, only to be just a teensy bit disappointed with how they came out? Here's the place to record what you'd do differently next time.

Are you the kind of knitter for whom a project just isn't complete until you've documented it in some way? Or are you looking for a place to take quiet pride in your creations?

Then this book is for you.

Let it meet your own personal knitting needs: make notes on works in progress, record ideas for future undertakings, sketch out that kilim carpet pattern that would make a wonderful, exotic pullover. Here are blank pages for your most cherished accomplishments or your wildest "someday" fantasy projects, charts for dream designs, and more practical pages for recording the contents of a modest or a truly outrageous yarn stash, the page number and issue number where you spotted that cardigan you must remember to start, the number of skeins you need the next time that great sock yarn is on sale.

If you can't draw a straight line, take heart—here, too, are templates for tracing basic knitwear shapes you can color in, knit-friendly graph paper for charting designs, and pages for recording your loved ones' measurements, along with charts and checklists for keeping track of which books and pieces of equipment and supplies you have, and which ones you can ask for the next time someone says, "What would you like for your birthday?"

Dream, draw, dabble, and design—it's all up to you.

Knitting Needle Sizes

Needle sizes can be confusing, because U.S. and English sizes run opposite one another, and many needles are marked only with their diameter in millimeters. Just remember, whatever size it takes you to knit at your desired gauge is the right size.

U.S.	METRIC	ENGLISH
0	2 mm	14
1	2¼ mm	13
	2½ mm	
2	2¾ mm	12
	3 mm	
3	3¼ mm	11
4	3½ mm	10
5	3¾ mm	9
	4 mm	
6		8
7	4½ mm	7
8	5 mm	6
9	5½ mm	5
10	6 mm	4
10½	6½ mm	2
	7 mm	
	7½ mm	
11	8 mm	1
13	9 mm	00
15	10 mm	0000
17	12¾ mm	
19	16 mm	
35	19 mm	
50	25½ mm	

Needle Notes

You could knit with a stick from your back yard, if you were desperate, or a pencil, or a child's pick-up sticks (in fact, these make good, cheap, double-points). But it's a lot more efficient and pleasing to the hand, eye, and spirit to use smooth, well-balanced needles made for this purpose. Whether you select plastic, wood, bamboo, casein, or metal, or use your great-grandmother's celluloid or ivory needles is a matter of your budget, your esthetics, the speed at which you knit, and the fiber you're using. Wood and bamboo, for instance, grip the yarn lightly, and are thus great for slippery fibers like cotton and silk; nickel-plated needles are favored by speedy knitters, and elegant, hand-turned exotic wooden needles lend a sense of luxury to the whole process.

It's both economical and creatively satisfying to produce some of your own knitting materials. If you can make your own knitting needles out of hardwood dowels, for instance, you will never run out of needles and can knit away on tools that express your own personality. Wooden dowels are available in craft stores and home supply shops in a variety of diameters, and woodworker's specialty supply stores often carry dowels in exotic woods that are excellent for this purpose.

Use a needle gauge to find the size you need, and cut them to the desired length with a coping saw or chop saw. Point the business end (both ends, for double-point needles) with a pencil sharpener, rounding the tip to your preference with a bit of sandpaper. Sand the shaft of the needle smooth, then rub with furniture paste, beeswax, or rub vigorously—as if sanding—with a piece of wax paper.

This is an excellent way to produce enough needles economically for a knitting class. Children who want to learn to knit can easily have their own needles in just the right diameters and lengths for little hands, and with their own creative touches.

For single-point needles, use hot glue to attach a bead, button, cork, marble, or other treasure to the non-working end. Wooden pegs or beads are ideal for this purpose, and can be colored with felt-tip pens and then sealed with clear nail polish.

Templates for Drawing Knittables

Trace these templates and use them to help you draw your spectacular knitwear. Tip: Trace these shapes as you need them and cut them out of large reusable sticky notes, then stick them in the back of the book when not in use.

Where is it
written that socks
have to match? Think
of all the time you can
save by just grabbing
your two favorite
ones from the
drawer...

Your mother was right —you should put on a hat.

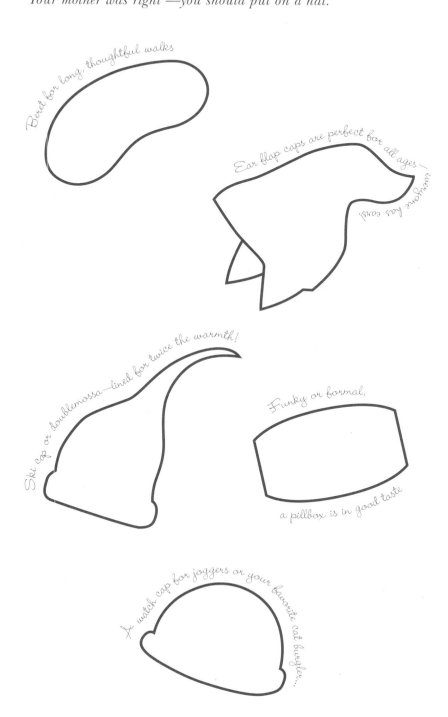

Beret for long, thoughtful walks

Ear flap caps are perfect for all ages — everyone has ears!

Ski cap or doublemossa—lined for twice the warmth!

Funky or formal, a pillbox is in good taste

A watch cap for joggers or your favorite cat burglar...

Think of gloves and mittens as miniature, wearable artist's canvases. Because they take so little time, mittens and gloves are the perfect place to try a new technique (lace? entrelac? intricate cabling?), a fine gauge, or a luxury fiber.

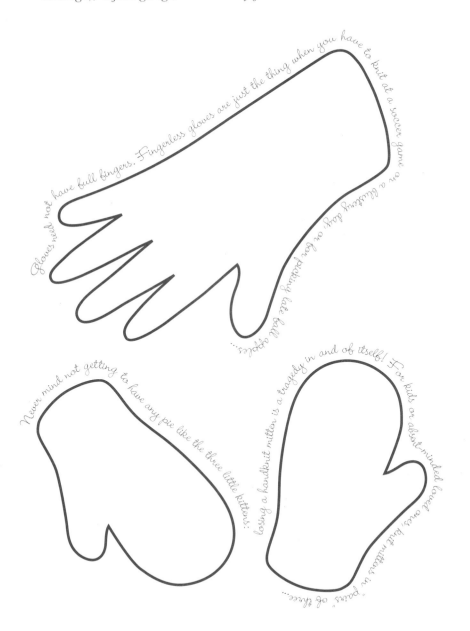

Gloves need not have full fingers. Fingerless gloves are just the thing when you have to knit at a soccer game or a blustery dog run or for packing late fall apples...

Never mind not getting to have any pie like the three little kittens...

...losing a handknit mitten is a tragedy in and of itself! For kids or absent-minded loved ones, knit mittens in pairs of three...

Trace these sweater templates, and then fiddle with them to help you draw cardigans and pullovers, V-necks and turtlenecks, boxy or tailored designs.

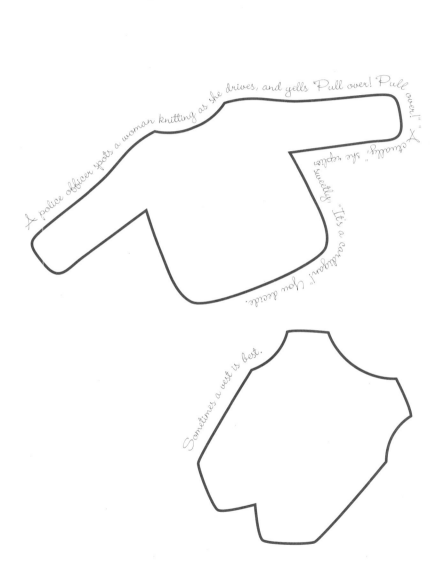

A police officer spots a woman knitting as she drives, and yells "Pull over! Pull over!" "Actually," she replies sweetly, "It's a cardigan." You decide.

Sometimes a vest is best.

Graphing Your Designs

Use the graph paper included here to chart design repeats or other figures to incorporate into your knitted masterpieces. Plain graph paper is fine for many projects, but knitted stitches are rarely exactly square. To use the graph which will most accurately represent your finished project, knit a swatch without the pattern, and calculate your stitch and row gauges.

If the number of stitches per inch equals the number of rows per inch, the plain graph paper's square gauge will be about right. If, however, your stitch gauge is higher than your row gauge (for instance, 5 stitches per inch and 4 rows per inch), your stitches will be taller than they are wide, and you should use the knitter's paper oriented so that each stitch is tall and narrow like a door. If your stitch gauge is lower than your row gauge (e.g., 4 stitches and 5 rows per inch), orient the knitters' graph paper so that the stitches are wide and squat, like a brick.

Finer yarn will show off a highly detailed design to greater advantage than a heavier yarn will, but the only way to find out whether it will please you when it is knitted up is to calculate your gauge, select the right graph paper, chart the design, and then knit a sample swatch with the correct colors or stitch patterns.

The wool upon his back, sir,
It reached up to the sky,
The eagles built their nests there,
For I heard the young ones cry.

—THE DARBY RAM (TRADITIONAL)

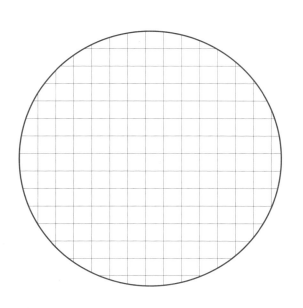

Knitting in the wings of a theater is thought to bring bad luck.

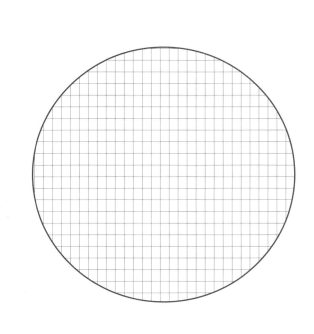

Baa baa white lamb
Have you any wool?
Yes, yes, dear child
I have a sackful
Holiday coat for Father
Sunday skirt for Mother
And two pairs of stockings
For little, little brother.

—TRADITIONAL SWEDISH NURSERY RHYME

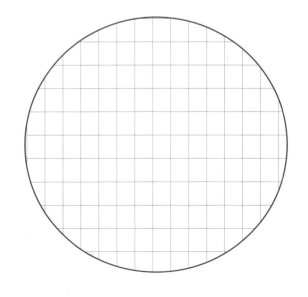

Empty needles invite bad luck. Cast on for a new project as soon as you've bound off a completed one.

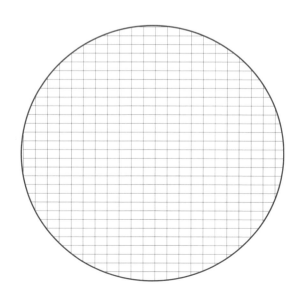

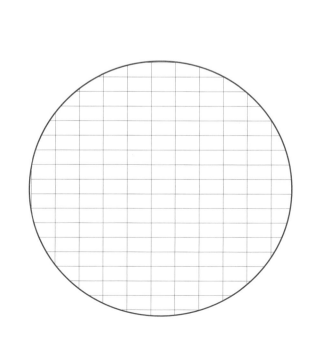

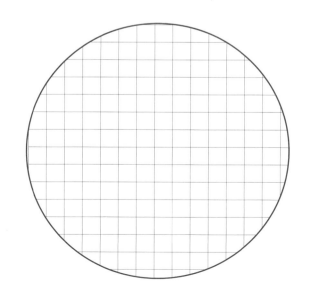

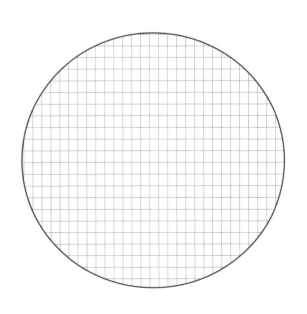

Wart dragged off to the tower room, where Merlyn was busy knitting himself a woolen night cap for the winter.

"I cast off two together at every other line," said the magician, "but for some reason it seems to end too sharply. Like an onion. It is the turning of the heel that does one, every time."

—T. H. WHITE, *THE ONCE AND FUTURE KING*

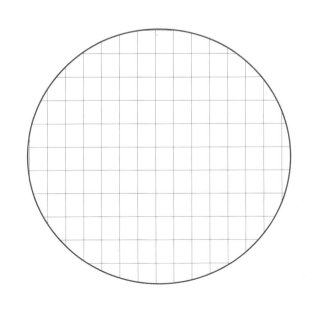

Nothing is horrider than a tight mitten.

—ELIZABETH ZIMMERMAN, *KNITTER'S ALMANAC*

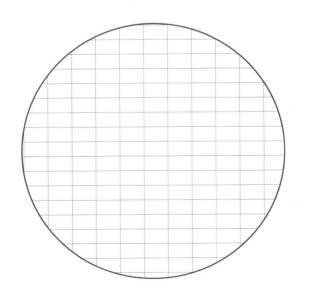

Pregnant knitters in Japan are warned against working with fine yarn, lest it strain the eyes of both baby and mother.

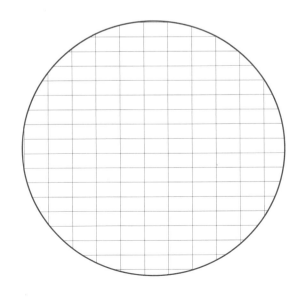

On the women sat, knitting, knitting. Darkness encompassed them . . . where they were to sit, knitting, knitting, counting the dropping heads.

—CHARLES DICKENS, *A TALE OF TWO CITIES*

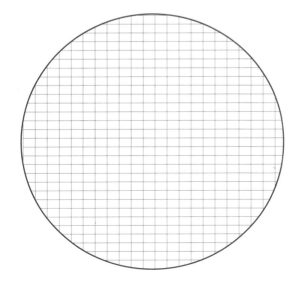

Navajo knitters make one deliberate error in a garment so as not to offend the gods with human attempts at perfection.

beauty is beauty
twice over
and good things are doubly
good
when you are talking about a pair of wool
socks
in the dead of winter.

—PABLO NERUDA, "ODE TO A PAIR OF SOCKS," IN *ODES TO COMMON THINGS*

Over the fence
Catch the sheep
Lead him through
And off he leaps

—TRADITIONAL RHYME FOR TEACHING THE KNIT STITCH

Patterns which wind clockwise are supposed to bring good luck.

Needle Inventory

Circulars. *Circular needles aren't just for knitting in the round. Knitting back and forth on a circular needle is easy on your wrists, makes for more portable knitting, and diminishes the likelihood that you'll poke the person next to you on the sofa or the airplane. Zip-type bags are great for storing circular needles, and so are the fly fishing line cases you can buy at sporting goods stores. To unkink a circular needle that's been coiled for a long time, hold the plastic part in a bowl of very hot tap water for a few minutes, then run your fingers along its length to make it straighter.*

LENGTH:	13"	16"	20"	24"/32"	40"	47"	60"
US SIZE							
000							
0							
1							
2							
3							
4							
5							
6							
7							
8							
9							
10							
10½							
11							
13							
15							
17							
19							
35							

Single Points. *Of course, you can knit a dishcloth on a 14-inch needle, or try to cram all the stitches of an adult's cardigan back on a 10-inch needle, but you'll make life easier if you select the right length for the project at hand. Straight needles travel well in specially made, rollable fabric cases, but they're equally at home in fine porcelain vases, jam jars (sorting roughly by size helps), cylindrical potato chip cans, or cylindrical metal or cardboard cases you can find sometimes in art supply stores or toy shops. Be careful to store wooden, celluloid, casein, or ivory needles in a cool place out of direct sunlight.*

LENGTH:	9–10"	14"
US SIZE		
000		
0		
1		
2		
3		
4		
5		
6		
7		
8		
9		
10		
10½		
11		
13		
15		
17		
19		
35		

Double Points. *Double pointed needles, which come in sets of 4 or 5, are used primarily for knitting small items (like socks and mittens) in the round. Because they tend to be shorter than single points, they also make fine needles for little hands when teaching a child to knit, or for working up swatches or I-cord—just put a point protector on the "extra" end to keep stitches from slipping off. Glove needles are extra short dp needles for working the fingers of gloves; they typically come in a set containing 2 or 3 diameters for different weights of yarn. Lace knitters may want to invest in fine steel dps, or "wires."*

LENGTH:	5–6"	7–9"	10"
US SIZE			
000			
0			
1			
2			
3			
4			
5			
6			
7			
8			
9			
10			
10½			
11			
13			
15			
17			
19			
35			

Yarn Shops and Vendors

NAME:

ADDRESS:

PHONE: FAX:

E-MAIL:

WEB SITE:

NOTES:

NAME:

ADDRESS:

PHONE: FAX:

E-MAIL:

WEB SITE:

NOTES:

NAME:

ADDRESS:

PHONE: FAX:

E-MAIL:

WEB SITE:

NOTES:

NAME:

ADDRESS:

PHONE: FAX:

E-MAIL:

WEB SITE:

NOTES:

Where Did I See That Pattern?

PATTERN: _____

SOURCE: _____

DESCRIPTION: _____

RECOMMENDED YARN(S): _____

_____

_____

YARN YARDAGE AND WEIGHT: _____

RECIPIENT: _____

SIZE: _____

SKETCH:

PATTERN: _____

SOURCE: _____

DESCRIPTION: _____

RECOMMENDED YARN(S): _____

_____

_____

YARN YARDAGE AND WEIGHT: _____

RECIPIENT: _____

SIZE: _____

SKETCH:

PATTERN:

SOURCE:

DESCRIPTION:

RECOMMENDED YARN(S):

YARN YARDAGE AND WEIGHT:

RECIPIENT:

SIZE:

SKETCH:

PATTERN:

SOURCE:

DESCRIPTION:

RECOMMENDED YARN(S):

YARN YARDAGE AND WEIGHT:

RECIPIENT:

SIZE:

SKETCH:

PATTERN: _____

SOURCE: _____

DESCRIPTION: _____

RECOMMENDED YARN(S): _____

_____

_____

YARN YARDAGE AND WEIGHT: _____

RECIPIENT: _____

SIZE: _____

SKETCH:

PATTERN: _____

SOURCE: _____

DESCRIPTION: _____

RECOMMENDED YARN(S): _____

_____

_____

YARN YARDAGE AND WEIGHT: _____

RECIPIENT: _____

SIZE: _____

SKETCH:

PATTERN:

SOURCE:

DESCRIPTION:

RECOMMENDED YARN(S):

YARN YARDAGE AND WEIGHT:

RECIPIENT:

SIZE:

SKETCH:

PATTERN:

SOURCE:

DESCRIPTION:

RECOMMENDED YARN(S):

YARN YARDAGE AND WEIGHT:

RECIPIENT:

SIZE:

SKETCH:

What Size Should I Knit?

NAME: _____ AGE: _____

CHEST: _____

NECK TO WAIST: _____

NECK TO HIP: _____

SHOULDER TO WRIST: _____

NECK TO WRIST: _____

UNDERARM TO WAIST: _____

UNDERARM TO HIP: _____

HEAD CIRCUMFERENCE: _____

FOOT, HEEL TO TOE: _____

WRIST TO TIP OF MIDDLE FINGER: _____

CIRCUMFERENCE OF PALM: _____

NAME: _____ AGE: _____

CHEST: _____

NECK TO WAIST: _____

NECK TO HIP: _____

SHOULDER TO WRIST: _____

NECK TO WRIST: _____

UNDERARM TO WAIST: _____

UNDERARM TO HIP: _____

HEAD CIRCUMFERENCE: _____

FOOT, HEEL TO TOE: _____

WRIST TO TIP OF MIDDLE FINGER: _____

CIRCUMFERENCE OF PALM: _____

NAME: _____ AGE: _____

CHEST: _____

NECK TO WAIST: _____

NECK TO HIP: _____

SHOULDER TO WRIST: _____

NECK TO WRIST: _____

UNDERARM TO WAIST: _____

UNDERARM TO HIP: _____

HEAD CIRCUMFERENCE: _____

FOOT, HEEL TO TOE: _____

WRIST TO TIP OF MIDDLE FINGER: _____

CIRCUMFERENCE OF PALM: _____

NAME: _____ AGE: _____

CHEST: _____

NECK TO WAIST: _____

NECK TO HIP: _____

SHOULDER TO WRIST: _____

NECK TO WRIST: _____

UNDERARM TO WAIST: _____

UNDERARM TO HIP: _____

HEAD CIRCUMFERENCE: _____

FOOT, HEEL TO TOE: _____

WRIST TO TIP OF MIDDLE FINGER: _____

CIRCUMFERENCE OF PALM: _____

NAME: _____ AGE: _____

CHEST: _____

NECK TO WAIST: _____

NECK TO HIP: _____

SHOULDER TO WRIST: _____

NECK TO WRIST: _____

UNDERARM TO WAIST: _____

UNDERARM TO HIP: _____

HEAD CIRCUMFERENCE: _____

FOOT, HEEL TO TOE: _____

WRIST TO TIP OF MIDDLE FINGER: _____

CIRCUMFERENCE OF PALM: _____

NAME: _____ AGE: _____

CHEST: _____

NECK TO WAIST: _____

NECK TO HIP: _____

SHOULDER TO WRIST: _____

NECK TO WRIST: _____

UNDERARM TO WAIST: _____

UNDERARM TO HIP: _____

HEAD CIRCUMFERENCE: _____

FOOT, HEEL TO TOE: _____

WRIST TO TIP OF MIDDLE FINGER: _____

CIRCUMFERENCE OF PALM: _____

SUPPLY CHECKLIST

- ☐ BAGS FOR BIG PROJECTS

- ☐ SMALL BAGS OR POUCHES FOR TAKE-ALONG PROJECTS

- ☐ EVEN SMALLER BAGS FOR NOTIONS

- ☐ STITCH GAUGE

- ☐ NEEDLE GAUGE

- ☐ STITCH HOLDERS

- ☐ POINT PROTECTORS

- ☐ STITCH/ROW COUNTER

- ☐ SEWING NEEDLES IN CASE

- ☐ KNITTING NEEDLE CASES OR ROLLS

- ☐ YARN/TAPESTRY NEEDLES (BLUNT)

- ☐ CROCHET HOOKS

- ☐ SCISSORS

- ☐ STITCH MARKERS

- ☐ BLOCKING PINS

- ☐ BLOCKING WIRES

- ☐ COIL-LESS SAFETY PINS

- ☐ PERSONALIZED GARMENT LABELS

- ☐ SMALL CALCULATOR

- ☐ PEN OR PENCIL AND PAPER

- ☐ HAND LOTION

- ☐ NAIL FILE OR EMERY BOARD

- ☐ _____

- ☐ _____

- ☐ _____

Commonly Used Knitting Abbreviations

alt	alternate	*opp*	opposite
approx	approximately	*oz*	ounce(s)
b	bobble	*p*	purl
bc	back cross	*p2tog*	purl 2 together
bo	bind off	*psso*	pass slipped stitch over
		pwise	purlwise, as if to purl
cab	cable		
cc	contrasting color	*rc*	right cross
cm	centimeter(s)	*rem*	remaining
cn	cable needle	*rep*	repeat
co	cast on	*rev stst*	reverse stockinette stitch
cont	continue	*RS*	right side
		rnd(s)	round(s)
dec	decrease, decreasing		
dpn	double-pointed needle(s)	*sk*	skip
		skn	skein
fc	front cross	*skp*	slip one, knit one, pass
foll	following		slipped stitch over
		sl	slip
g	grams	*ssk*	slip, slip, knit
		st(s)	stitch(es)
inc	increase, increasing	*stst*	stockinette (or stocking)
		stitch	
k	knit		
kbl, ktbl	knit through back of loop	*tbl*	through back of loop
k2tog	knit 2 together	*tog*	together
kwise	knitwise, as if to knit		
		WS	wrong side
lc	left cross	*wyib*	with yarn in back
lh	left hand	*wyif*	with yarn in front
		yf	yarn forward
m	meter(s)	*yo*	yarn over
m1	make one	*yo2*	yarn over twice
mb	make bobble	*	repeat instructions as
mc	main color		often as indicated
		[ ]	repeat instructions inside
no	number		brackets as often
			as indicated